BASIC / NOT BORING

SPELLING

Grades 2-3

Inventive Exercises to Sharpen Skills and Raise Achievement

Series Concept & Development
by Imogene Forte & Marjorie Frank
Exercises by Marjorie Frank

Incentive Publications, Inc.
Nashville, Tennessee

About the cover:
Bound resist, or tie dye, is the most ancient known method of fabric surface design. The brilliance of the basic tie dye design on this cover reflects the possibilities that emerge from the mastery of basic skills.

Illustrated by Kathleen Bullock
Cover art by Mary Patricia Deprez, dba Tye Dye Mary®
Cover design by Marta Drayton, Joe Shibley, and W. Paul Nance
Edited by Jennifer J. Streams

ISBN 0-86530-442-4

PRINTED IN THE UNITED STATES OF AMERICA
www.incentivepublications.com

TABLE OF CONTENTS

Appendix

CELEBRATE BASIC LANGUAGE SKILLS

Basic does not mean boring! There is certainly nothing dull about . . .
- . . . sorting out vowel spellings with a weight lifter, a mountain climber, and a pirate
- . . . paying a visit to Bigfoot for help with a spelling puzzle
- . . . helping a wizard or Jungle Jane with some tricky word endings
- . . . traveling back in time to the stone age to seek out some good spelling
- . . . paying a visit to a frog's dream to search for silent letters
- . . . searching for prefixes and suffixes in dangerous, deep ocean waters
- . . . lending a hand to a crab who's having some spelling trouble
- . . . joining a friendly opossum, quail, and skunk to polish up spelling of O, W, & S words
- . . . tracking down misspelled words with a clever fox detective, a lovable bear, a spunky beaver, or some mischievous raccoons.

These are just some of the adventures students can explore as they celebrate basic spelling skills. The idea of celebrating the basics is just what it sounds like—enjoying and getting good at spelling in every day life. Each page invites young learners to try a high-interest, visually appealing exercise that will sharpen one or more specific spelling skills. This is not just any ordinary fill-in-the-blanks way to learn. These exercises are fun and surprising. Students will do the useful work of practicing spelling skills while they enjoy a variety of adventures with a delightful assortment of forest creatures.

The pages in this book can be used in many ways:
- to review or practice a spelling skill with one student
- to sharpen the skill with a small or large group
- to begin a lesson on a particular skill
- to assess how well a student has mastered a skill

Each page has directions that are written simply. It is intended that an adult be available to help students read the information on the page, if help is needed. In most cases, the pages will best be used as a follow-up to a lesson that has already been taught. The pages are excellent tools for immediate reinforcement and sharpening of a spelling rule or skill.

As your students take on the challenges of these adventures with spelling, they will grow! And as you watch them check off the basic language skills they've strengthened, you can celebrate with them.

The Skills Test

Use the skills test beginning on page 56 as a pre-test and/or a post-test. This will help you check the students' mastery of basic spelling skills and will prepare them for success on achievement tests.

SKILLS CHECKLIST
SPELLING, GRADES 2-3

✔	SKILL	PAGE(S)
	Correctly spell words with double consonants	10
	Correctly spell words with confusing initial consonants: c & s; c & k; j & g; s & z	11
	Correctly spell words with confusing initial blends: gh, ph	12
	Correctly spell words with double vowels	13
	Correctly spell words with special vowel combinations	14-19
	Correct words that are spelled incorrectly	15, 42
	Correctly spell words with special endings	20-21
	Correctly spell words with y and ey endings	22
	Correctly spell words with silent letters	23
	Correctly spell plural nouns	24, 25
	Correctly spell verbs in the past tense	26, 27
	Correctly spell verbs with ing endings	28
	Correctly spell comparative adjectives (er and est endings)	29
	Correctly spell words with prefixes	30
	Correctly spell words with suffixes	31
	Distinguish among words that sound alike: homonyms	32, 33
	Identify, spell, and form compound words	34, 35
	Spell contractions correctly	36
	Distinguish between words that are easily confused with one another	37
	Correctly spell words in which the letter S is prominent	38
	Correctly spell words in which the letter Q is prominent	39
	Correctly spell words in which the letter O is prominent	40
	Correctly spell words with the letters W, X, Y, or Z as prominent letters	41
	Correctly spell big words	42
	Correctly spell small words	43
	Correctly spell proper names	44, 45
	Correctly spell difficult words	46
	Correctly spell food words	47
	Correctly spell number words	48
	Correctly spell animal names	49
	Identify words spelled correctly	50; also 11, 15, 33, 38, 46
	Identify words spelled incorrectly	51; also 37, 38, 52, 53, 54
	Identify and correct incorrect spelling in written pieces	52, 53, 54

SPELLING

Grades 2-3

Skills Exercises

h...i...b...e...r...n...a...

Double the Fun

The McFrog twins have more than double the ice cream they usually get!
Their cones are full of double-good words, too.
All the words in the cones are missing pairs of double letters.
Find the right pair for each group of words. Write the letters in the blanks.

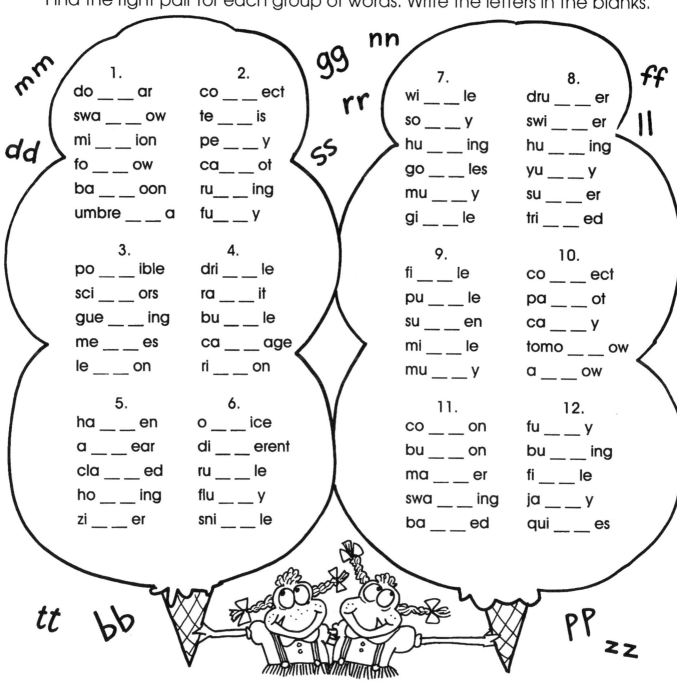

mm *gg* *nn*

dd *rr* *ss* *ff* *ll*

1.
do _ _ ar
swa _ _ ow
mi _ _ ion
fo _ _ ow
ba _ _ oon
umbre _ _ a

2.
co _ _ ect
te _ _ is
pe _ _ y
ca _ _ ot
ru _ _ ing
fu _ _ y

7.
wi _ _ le
so _ _ y
hu _ _ ing
go _ _ les
mu _ _ y
gi _ _ le

8.
dru _ _ er
swi _ _ er
hu _ _ ing
yu _ _ y
su _ _ er
tri _ _ ed

3.
po _ _ ible
sci _ _ ors
gue _ _ ing
me _ _ es
le _ _ on

4.
dri _ _ le
ra _ _ it
bu _ _ le
ca _ _ age
ri _ _ on

9.
fi _ _ le
pu _ _ le
su _ _ en
mi _ _ le
mu _ _ y

10.
co _ _ ect
pa _ _ ot
ca _ _ y
tomo _ _ ow
a _ _ ow

5.
ha _ _ en
a _ _ ear
cla _ _ ed
ho _ _ ing
zi _ _ er

6.
o _ _ ice
di _ _ erent
ru _ _ le
flu _ _ y
sni _ _ le

11.
co _ _ on
bu _ _ on
ma _ _ er
swa _ _ ing
ba _ _ ed

12.
fu _ _ y
bu _ _ ing
fi _ _ le
ja _ _ y
qui _ _ es

tt *bb*

pp *zz*

Name _____

How Do You Spell Magic?

Milton the Magician is pulling words out of his magic hat instead of rabbits. In each pair or group of words, one has used the WRONG letter to make the sound s or z or k or g.

Circle the word from each pair that is spelled RIGHT.

4. sircle circle	5. crasy crazy	6. size sise	7. abcent absent	8. cloudy kloudy

20. jentle gentle

9. giant jiant

19. krayon crayon

1. majic magic magik

2. surprise surprize

Presto!

10. gym jym

18. city sity

3. circus cirkus sircus

11. jelly gelly

17. cool kool

12. jiraffe giraffe

16. kolor color	15. catch katch	14. tease teaze	13. eyes eyze

Name _____

Confusing Consonants (c & s, c & k, j & g, s & z)

Confusing Pairs

Ralph and Fulbright like to hop on the rocks in this rushing stream.
To help them, you need to finish the spelling words with the letters *ph* or *gh*.
Be careful, because *ph* and *gh* often make the same sound.

Ralph will only step on words with the letters *ph*. Color these stones RED.
Fulbright only steps on words with the letters *gh*. Color these stones BLUE.

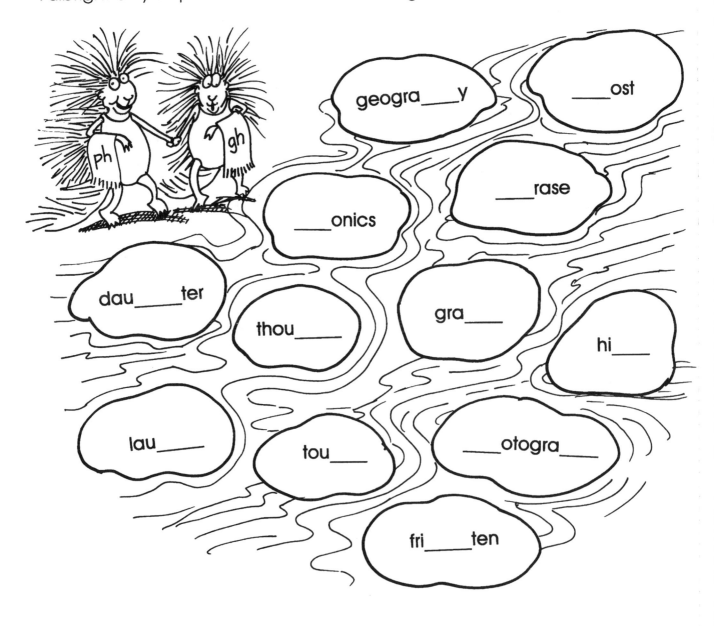

Name _____

Confusing Consonant Pairs (gh & ph)

Copyright ©2000 by Incentive Publications, Inc., Nashville, TN.
Basic Skills/Spelling 2-3

Twice the Trouble

Mr. Moose is seeing double today.
All the words on his eye test are missing their vowels.
He can see them. Can you?
Write the missing vowels.

EYE CHART

OO oo oo EE EE EE

1. aftern _____ n

2. br _____ ze

3. d _____ rknob

4. fr _____ zer

5. kn _____

6. oversl _____ p

7. g _____ se

8. outd _____ rs

9. ch _____ sy

10. dr _____ l

11. r _____ ster

12. squ _____ ze

13. bl _____ m

14. f _____ lish

15. sp _____ ch

16. c _____ l

17. st _____ p

18. qu _____ n

19. racc _____ n

20. bab _____ n

21. t _____ th

22. p _____ k

23. l _____ se

24. cart _____ n

25. sch _____ l

26. ball _____ n

27. coc _____ n

Name _____

Double Vowels

The Sleepy Letter

What a strange dream Jake is having!
Usually he dreams in pictures, but tonight he is dreaming of words.
Some of the words have a sleepy letter that makes no sound—the silent e.
Read each word. If it contains a silent e, color that section of Jake's dream.

Name _____

Words with Silent e

Basic Skills/Spelling 2-3

Weighty Words

Waldo is having trouble with his weights! His spelling is in trouble, too!
Maybe it's because he has forgotten the spelling rule on the barbells.
Review the rule about using *i* and *e* in spelling words.
Then use the rule to find the words below Waldo that are
spelled CORRECTLY.
Circle them in red.
The words above Waldo are rule-breakers! They do not follow the *ie* rule.
Choose the right spelling for each one. Circle it in red.

1. height
   hieght

2. weird
   wierd

3. either
   iether

4. neither
   niether

5. foriegn
   foreign

6. cieling
   ceiling

RULE:
i comes before
e,
except
after c

or when
sounding like
A, as in
"neighbor" or
"weigh"

lie	neice	veil	vein	cieling	weight
their	piece	grieve	biege	brief	peice
breif	eight	freight	nieghbor	believe	pie
recieve	reign	riendeer	sleigh	die	neighborhood

Name _____

Words With ie or ei

Vowels to Shout About

When he reached the top of this tough mountain, Chester shouted with joy!

Chester got to this top by following a path of words with the vowel pair *ou*.

Which words need the letters *ou* to be spelled correctly?

Fill in the blanks which need *ou*.

Then use a red marker to connect them.

This will show the path that Chester used to climb the mountain.

Yahoo!

sc___t

y___rs

sh___ld   h___se

r___nd   br___k

f__rful

sh___t

b___ght   w___ther   bl___se

s___nd

r___sonable

cl___n   m___th   th___ght

s___son   gr___nd   arg___ment

c___sin

f___ntain   p___son

ab___t

gr___n   rep___t

Name _____

Special Vowel Combinations (ou)   Copyright ©2000 by Incentive Publications, Inc., Nashville, TN.
Basic Skills/Spelling 2-3

Vowels to Boast About

Coach Roach loves to boast about his winning track team.
He also loves to use words with vowels that sound like the vowels in his name.
Read all the words on the track and field where his team practices.
Circle the words in which the vowel combination *oa* makes the same sound as it does in Coach's name.

GO!
GO!
GO!

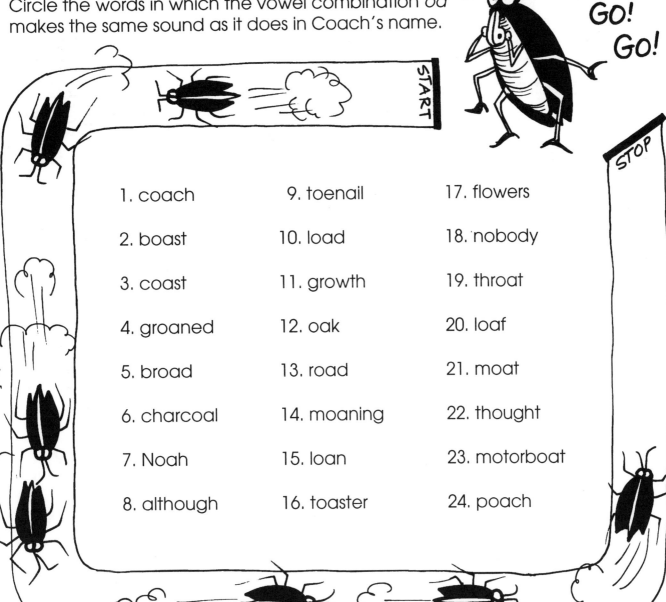

START

STOP

1. coach	9. toenail	17. flowers
2. boast	10. load	18. nobody
3. coast	11. growth	19. throat
4. groaned	12. oak	20. loaf
5. broad	13. road	21. moat
6. charcoal	14. moaning	22. thought
7. Noah	15. loan	23. motorboat
8. although	16. toaster	24. poach

Name _____

Vowels to Treasure

The map will help Felix find a buried treasure, if he can keep his vowels straight!

Follow the clues to draw a trail straight to the treasure.

Remember this: the trail goes ONLY to words with an *ea* vowel combination.

Look on the map for a word to match each clue.

Clue #1
 Begin at Cape Fear

Clue #2
 NE to opposite of late

Clue #3
 E to hair on chin

Clue #4
 NW to opposite of hard

Clue #5
 NE to looking hard

Clue #6
 SE to robbing

Clue #7
 W to a food

Clue #8
 N to summer & winter

Clue #9
 S to a wiggly animal

Clue #10
 SE to Use your lungs!

Clue # 11
 SE to rainy or sunny

Clue # 12
 N to a sandy place

Dig here for the treasure!

Mark the spot with X.

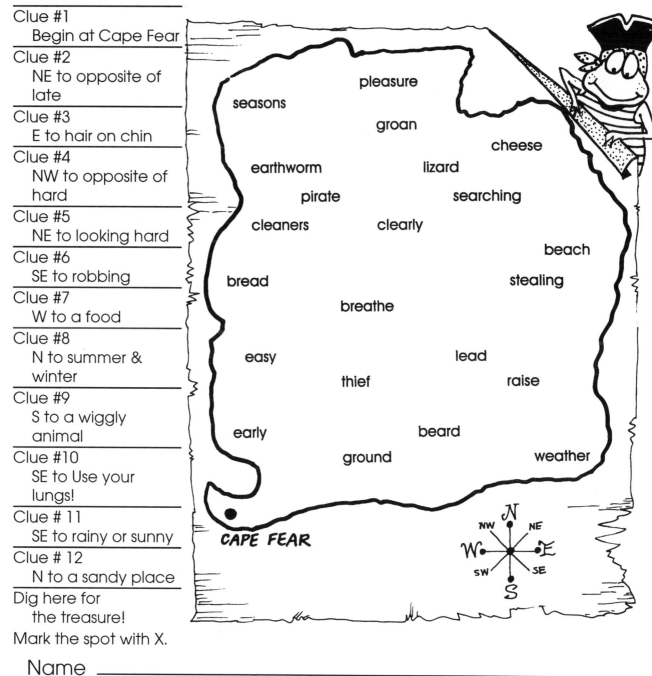

Name _____

Special Vowel Combinations (ea)

Copyright ©2000 by INCENTIVE PUBLICATIONS, Inc., Nashville, TN.
Basic Skills/Spelling 2-3

Vowels To Puzzle Over

Francie has a good reason to avoid this giant!

However, there isn't a reason to avoid these vowel pairs.

All the words in the puzzle contain one of these pairs.

The vowels are already in the puzzle. Follow the clues to finish the words!

CLUES

Down

1. It's_____ , it's pouring!
2. your mother's sister
3. letters and cards
4. sticky stuff
6. bothersome sounds
8. opposite of smile
10. clothing for swimming
11. dirt in the ground
12. color of ocean

Across

4. huge creature
5. houses and schools
7. sharp end of a pencil
9. to lift up
13. a river does this
14. end of a dog

Name _____

Special Vowel Combinations (ai, au, ia, ui, oi, ue, ow)

Star Power

Lila LeFrog is a singer. Lester Beaker is an actor.

The endings on *singer* and *actor* sound the same, but are not spelled the same.

An ending with this sound can be spelled with *er, or,* or *ar.*

Write the correct ending for each word on Lila and Lester's stage.

La-la-la-la
La-la-la

To be, or not to be...

1. col_____
2. rul_____
3. tow_____
4. liv_____
5. winn_____
6. doct_____
7. summ_____
8. od_____
9. doll_____
10. raz_____
11. teach_____
12. coll_____

13. mot_____
14. flav_____
15. ladd_____
16. sol_____
17. maj_____
18. riv_____
19. moth_____
20. fav_____
21. vot_____
22. nev_____
23. socc_____
24. tract_____

Name _____

Special Endings (er, or, ar)

Basic Skills/Spelling 2-3

Words to Recycle

To Gretta's surprise, the dumpster is full of words today, instead of food!

They were thrown into the trash because they have the wrong endings.

Help her get them out of the trash and recycle them by spelling them correctly. Follow the directions below the dumpster.

1. Write the words that should end in *age*. Spell them correctly.

   _____

2. Write the words that should end in *adge*. Spell them correctly.

   _____

3. Write the words that should end in *edge*. Spell them correctly.

   _____

4. Write the word that should end in *idge*. Spell it correctly.

   _____

5. Write the words that should end in *udge*. Spell them correctly.

   _____

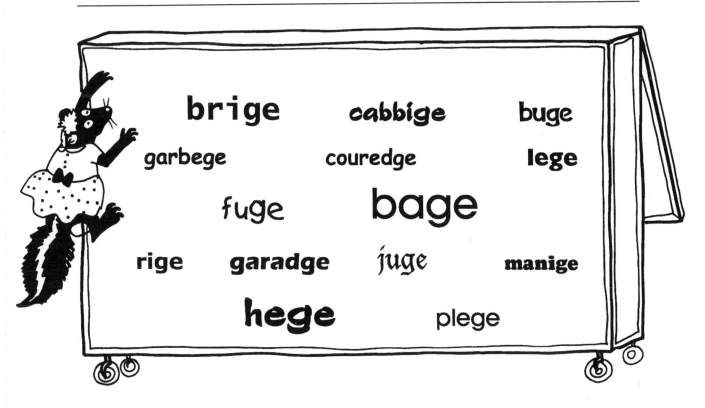

brige   cabbige   buge

garbege   couredge   lege

fuge   bage

rige   garadge   juge   manige

hege   plege

Name _____

Basic Skills/Spelling 2-3   **Special Endings (age, edge, udge, adge, idge)**

Wise About Ys

Are you wise about words that end in *y*?

Some words end in *y*. Some end in *ey*. In both kinds, the sound is the same.

Wilbur thinks he knows the right endings for all these words. Do you?

Write the correct ending.

Color the starbursts: yellow for *y* and purple for *ey*.

1. donk__

2. penn__

3. likel__

4. lad___

5. reall__

6. monk___

7. mon__

8. ic___

9. cit__

10. cheer___

11. tin__

12. hon__

13. sill__

14. turk__

15. speed__

16. vall___

17. berr__

18. cop___

Name _____

Special Endings (y and ey)

Basic Skills/Spelling 2-3

Straight to the Hive

All of Bruno's bees are buzzing as they head for the hive.

However, some of the letters in the path are NOT making any sound.

The bee path has many words that contain one or more silent letters.

Read the words. CROSS OUT any words that do NOT have a silent letter.

kneel
thumb
knot
rhyme
wrap
wrong
cave
never
knife
liver
bridge
honest
halo
dough
knight
sword
wishes
cola
combing
doorknob
stretch
ghost
gasping
crumb
wrote
lamb
slippery
knuckle
climb
knees
shape
laugh
lumpy
whisper
whine
tassle
limbs

Name _____

Plenty of Balloons

Each balloon in Buddy's bunch has a word that means ONE of something.
Make each word into a plural (more than one) by following the rule.
Each one you get right will help Buddy float even higher in the air.

If you added *s* to a word, color the balloon red, yellow, or blue.
If you added *es* to a word, color the balloon orange, purple, or green.

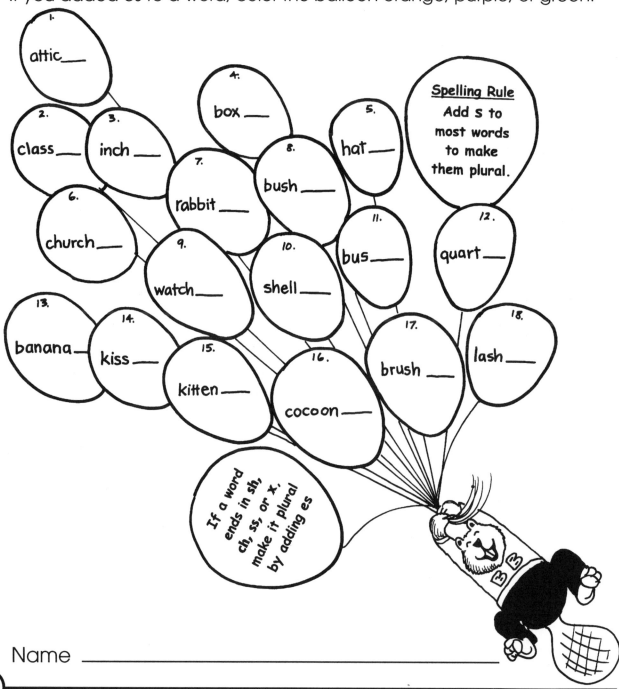

1. attic___
2. class___
3. inch___
4. box___
5. hat___
6. church___
7. rabbit___
8. bush___
9. watch___
10. shell___
11. bus___
12. quart___
13. banana___
14. kiss___
15. kitten___
16. cocoon___
17. brush___
18. lash___

Spelling Rule
Add s to most words to make them plural.

If a word ends in sh, ch, ss, or x, make it plural by adding es

Name _____

Plural Nouns

Basic Skills/Spelling 2-3

A Sky Full of Plurals

At the kite flying contest, three kites are left in the sky.
Each one has a spelling rule written on it.
Look at each word on the word list and decide which kite it matches.
Write the word in a plural form on one of the bows on
that kite. Spell it right!

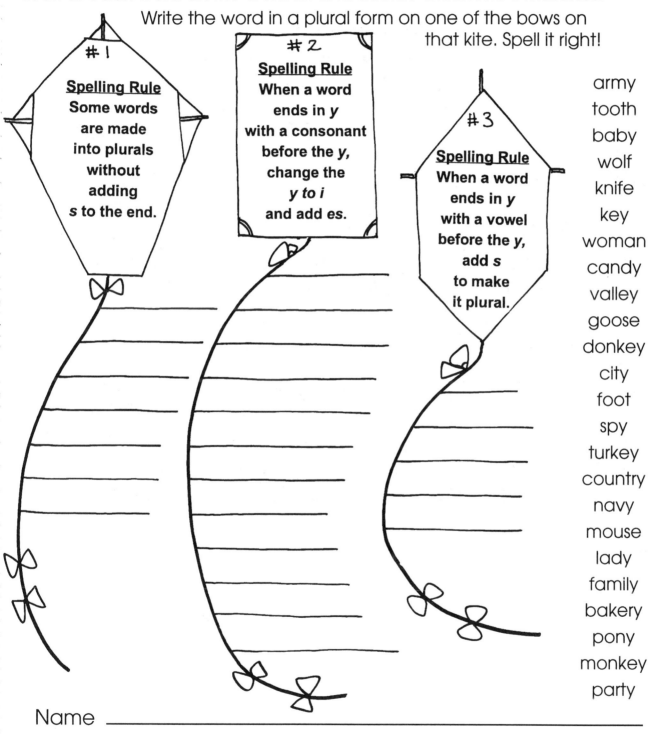

#1
Spelling Rule
Some words
are made
into plurals
without
adding
s to the end.

#2
Spelling Rule
When a word
ends in *y*
with a consonant
before the *y*,
change the
y to i
and add *es*.

#3
Spelling Rule
When a word
ends in *y*
with a vowel
before the *y*,
add *s*
to make
it plural.

army
tooth
baby
wolf
knife
key
woman
candy
valley
goose
donkey
city
foot
spy
turkey
country
navy
mouse
lady
family
bakery
pony
monkey
party

Name _____

Words from the Past

The Frogstone family had a very busy life many, many years ago.
Adding *ed* to the words will show that their activities happened in the past.
Follow the rules to write each word in the past tense.

SPELLING RULES

- **To change most words to past tense, add *ed*.**
- **If a word ends in *y* with a consonant before the *y*, change the *y to i* before adding *ed*. (*cry---cried*)**
- **If a word ends in a consonant with one vowel before it, double the consonant and add *ed*. (*sag--sagged*)**

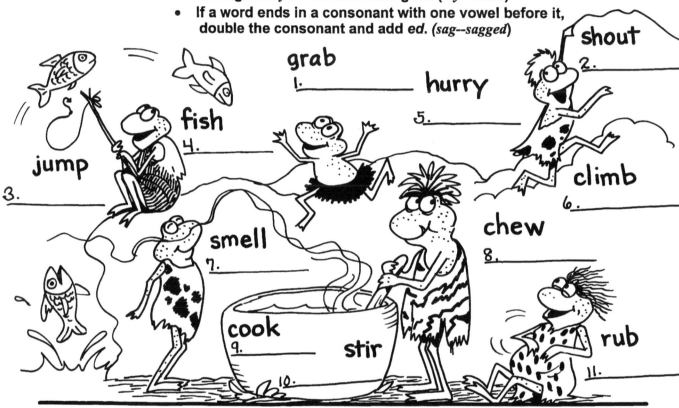

grab
1. _____

shout
2. _____

jump
3. _____

fish
4. _____

hurry
5. _____

climb
6. _____

smell
7. _____

chew
8. _____

cook
9. _____

stir
10. _____

rub
11. _____

12. try _____

13. follow _____

14. wish _____

15. deny _____

16. sniff _____

17. worry _____

18. slip _____

19. rest _____

20. trim _____

21. rob _____

22. enjoy _____

23. laugh _____

Name _____

Verbs in the Past Tense

Basic Skills/Spelling 2-3

More Words from the Past

Change these present-day statements to the past tense.
This will show what Frederick Stonefrog and his pet dinosaur did a long, long time ago.

All of these are words that do not follow the usual rules for past tense.

Be careful about the spelling of the new words!

1. I slide down a rock. Many years ago, Frederick _____ down a rock.

2. I leave for school. Many years ago, Frederick _____ for school.

3. I keep busy. Many years ago, Frederick _____ busy.

4. I shake hands. Many years ago, Frederick _____ hands.

5. I bite my food. Many years ago, Frederick _____ his food.

6. I eat lunch. Many years ago, Frederick _____ lunch.

7. I choose to laugh. Many years ago, Frederick _____ to laugh.

8. I build a fort. Many years ago, Frederick _____ a fort.

9. I teach swimming. Many years ago, Frederick _____ swimming.

10. I catch a cold. Many years ago, Frederick _____ a cold.

11. I find a friend. Many years ago, Frederick _____ a friend.

12. I lose a tooth. Many years ago, Frederick _____ teeth.

13. I see the sky. Many years ago, Frederick _____ the sky.

14. I hide in a cave. Many years ago, Frederick _____ in a cave.

Name _____

Endings that Swing

Jungle Jayne spends a lot of time swinging on vines and leaping between trees.

The words around her vines tell other things Jayne does.

Write each word again on the line below it, adding *ing* to each one.

Follow the rules to spell the words right.

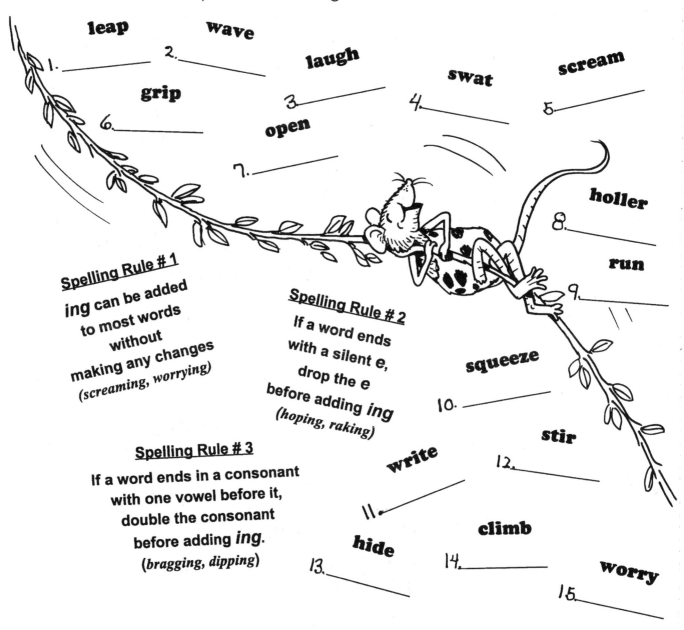

leap

1. _____

wave

2. _____

laugh

3. _____

swat

4. _____

scream

5. _____

grip

6. _____

open

7. _____

holler

8. _____

run

9. _____

squeeze

10. _____

write

11. _____

stir

12. _____

hide

13. _____

climb

14. _____

worry

15. _____

Spelling Rule # 1

ing can be added to most words without making any changes *(screaming, worrying)*

Spelling Rule # 2

If a word ends with a silent e, drop the e before adding **ing** *(hoping, raking)*

Spelling Rule # 3

If a word ends in a consonant with one vowel before it, double the consonant before adding **ing**. *(bragging, dipping)*

Name _____

Who's the Hungriest of All?

At the pie-eating contest, Herbert is the hungriest!
The word hungry changes as the eaters are compared.
Follow the rules to add *er* and *est* to each of the words!

Spelling Rule
If a word ends in a consonant with one vowel before it, double the consonant before adding **er** or **est**.
(hotter, reddest)

Spelling Rule
When a word ends in **y**, change the **y** to **i** before adding **er** or **est**.
(friendlier, tiniest)

hungry   **hungrier**   **hungriest**

1. sweet   _____   _____
2. tasty   _____   _____
3. big   _____   _____
4. grumpy   _____   _____
5. full   _____   _____
6. great   _____   _____
7. sticky   _____   _____
8. hot   _____   _____
9. fluffy   _____   _____
10. tall   _____   _____

Name _____

Comparative Adjectives

Underwater Discoveries

The divers are discovering some lost prefixes sinking below the waves.
For each word below, find the matching prefix in the waves.
Add the prefix to make a new word. Write the whole word on the line.

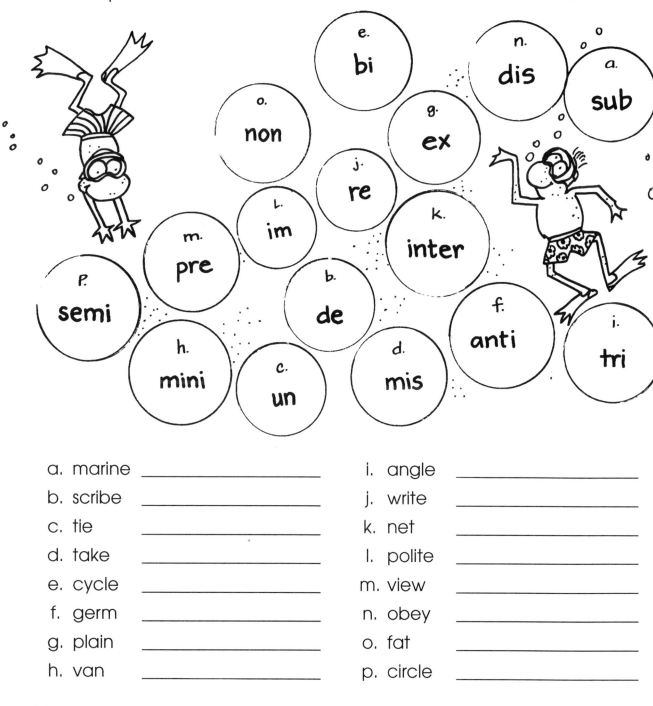

a. marine _____

b. scribe _____

c. tie _____

d. take _____

e. cycle _____

f. germ _____

g. plain _____

h. van _____

i. angle _____

j. write _____

k. net _____

l. polite _____

m. view _____

n. obey _____

o. fat _____

p. circle _____

Name _____

Dangerous Waters

How will Felix ever get off this island? The water is full of danger!
The suffix *ous* means full of. Add *ous* to the word danger, and you have
a word that describes Felix's problem!

Add the suffix to each of these words to make a new word.
Follow the rules, so that you get the new word spelled right.

Spelling Rule
**When a word ends with a silent e,
drop the e before adding a suffix—
if the suffix begins with a vowel.**
(love + able = lovable)
(drive + en = driven)

Spelling Rule
**When a word ends in y,
change the y to i
before adding a suffix.**
(grumpy + er = grumpier)
(shaky + ness = shakiness)

1. scare + y = _____

2. act + or = _____

3. differ + ent = _____

4. tropic + al = _____

5. lone + ly = _____

6. care + less = _____

7. friendly + ness = _____

8. trouble + some = _____

9. fame + ous = _____

10. shiny + est = _____

11. fright + en = _____

12. like + able = _____

13. fancy + er = _____

14. self + ish = _____

15. forget + ful = _____

16. friend + ship = _____

Name _____

Sound-Alike Words

GACK!

Did Polly meet a *bare* with *bear* feet or a *bear* with *bare* feet?
Was it a dark, stormy *knight* or a dark, stormy *night*?

Homonyms are words that sound alike.

When you use a homonym, make sure to spell it right!

Choose the right word for each sentence. Write the word in the blank.

1. (choose, chews) Did you _____ to walk alone in the woods at night?

2. (pail, pale) She could barely see in the _____ moonlight.

3. (grown, groan) Polly let out a loud _____ when she saw the big bear.

4. (so, sew, sow) She was _____ frightened that she could not move.

5. (fir, fur) The bear was covered with shaggy brown _____ .

6. (see, sea) It's a good thing Polly can _____ well in the dark!

7. (toe, tow) Is the bear angry because he stubbed his _____ on a log?

8. (pause, paws) Did you see those sharp claws on the bear's _____ ?

9. (aunts, ants) The fallen log is covered with crawling _____ .

10. (sense, cents) That bear has a great _____ of smell.

11. (prince, prints) The bear followed her foot _____ through the woods.

12. (road, rode) Polly ran along a winding _____ through the forest.

13. (shoe, shoo) As she ran, she lost a _____ in the dark.

14. (berry, bury) The bear stopped to pick a juicy _____ from a bush.

Name _____

Basic Skills/Spelling 2-3

Homonym Mix-Up

It is easy to get mixed up about words that sound alike. When Mildred wrote her story, she got many homonyms confused with other words that sound the same.

Find all the words that are spelled wrong.
Circle them in red.
Then write the correct word on one of the lines.

My story happened on a night when I was very board and wanted to do something fun. My friend Cricket and I decided we wood meat write at ate o'clock to go on an adventure to the creak. I meant to weight where I said I would, but I did knot.

Instead, I took a shortcut threw the prickly bushes to beet him there. This was a bad idea. Cricket maid it to the creek, but I never did.

My tale got tangled in the prickly bushes and eye was trapped all knight. Luckily, a pare of friendly mice came buy and set me free—or I might still be their!

Mine is a long, sad tale.

Name _____

Two Words Make New Words

The words in Oscar's favorite pond are words that have a special talent. They can be combined with other words to make compound words.

water + falls = waterfalls   **under + water = underwater**

For each group of words below, find a word in the pond that makes compound words from ALL the words.

bed   flash   shoe   band   any   home   water   sea   sand   finger   rain

A. _____ melon
   _____ falls
   _____ color
   _____ way
   _____ front

B. _____ nail
   _____ paint
   _____ print
   _____ tip

C. _____ bow
   _____ coat
   _____ drop
   _____ fall

D. _____ time
   _____ bug
   _____ room
   _____ spread
   _____ side

E. _____ box
   _____ bag
   _____ storm
   _____ pile

F. _____ lace
   horse _____
   _____ box
   snow _____

G. _____ body
   _____ thing
   _____ one
   _____ way
   _____ where

H. _____ shore
   _____ weed
   _____ shell
   _____ sick

I. _____ sick
   _____ work
   _____ made
   _____ grown

Name _____

Words with Fire

Bring some *firewood* to build a *campfire* in the *fireplace*!

Watch the *fireflies* and the *fireworks* by the *fireside*!

FIRE helps to make a lot of compound words!

What is the word that can make compound words for each of these groups?

Write that same word to make compounds from all the words in the line.

1. _____ mare over _____ _____ gown _____ time _____ light

2. camp _____ _____ side _____ doors knock _____ with _____

3. _____ fire _____ ground _____ site

4. sun _____ _____ house flash _____ day _____ _____ weight

5. _____ water _____ ground _____ line _____ pants

6. sun _____ _____ town _____ stairs _____ pour

7. _____ worm _____ store _____ case cook _____

8. _____ flake _____ man _____ ball _____ shoes

9. out _____ _____ step _____ bell _____ way

10. _____ light _____ down _____ burn _____ set _____ flower

Name _____

Catching Contractions

Cassie Crab has caught a net full of contractions today.
Some of them are not yet written in her net.
Write a contraction to match each word pair below.
Spell them right!

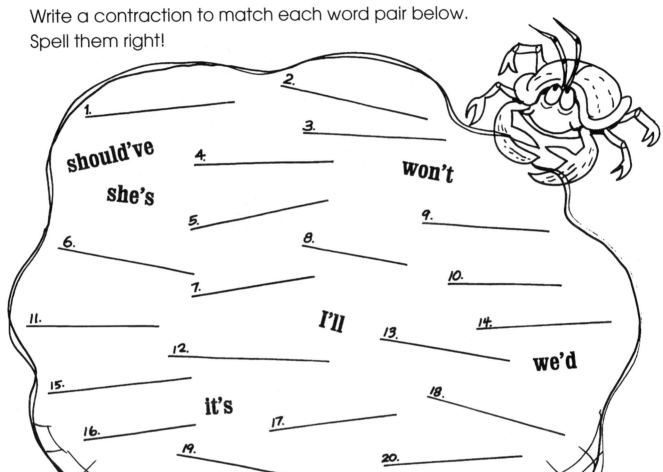

1. you are   6. were not   11. we would   16. you will

2. I have   7. who will   12. did not   17. they are

3. will not   8. was not   13. it will   18. cannot

4. she would   9. what is   14. could not   19. he will

5. let us   10. we are   15. that is   20. does not

Name _____

Confusing Words

A large pine cone hit Uncle Freddy on the head while he was napping.

This left Uncle Freddy very confused with his words. Every sentence he says has a wrong word.

Circle the wrong word. Write the correct word at the end of the sentence.

1. Witch day is it today, anyway?

2. The fresh air makes me so tried.

3. I like the quite afternoons in the forest.

4. I had tasty gooseberries for desert today.

5. It looks as if rainy whether is coming soon.

6. Please don't run away form me!

7. I have lost everything accept my head.

8. Can you crawl though that hollow log, Frankie?

9. I drank the whole cartoon of tasty cream.

10. Grandma Fox gave me her receipt for acorn stew.

11. Just look at those beautiful collars in the sunset!

12. Later today, I will write in my dairy.

1. _____
2. _____
3. _____
4. _____
5. _____
6. _____
7. _____
8. _____
9. _____
10. _____
11. _____
12. _____

Name _____

Surprise Over the Fence

Snoopy Sissy Skunk is spying on something over the fence.

What is it? Read the words in the puzzle to find out.

All the words contain the letter S. Some of them are spelled WRONG.

Color the CORRECT word spaces green.

Color the WRONG word spaces red or blue.

Sassy
mesy
Mississippi
misster
sandwitches
sirup
disease
possable
sisster
fussy
bussines
seeweed
mising
salid
sword
surprize
singel
hissing
pleese
scissors
seeson
sausage
sixthe
sentances
stranjer
sucess
seventey
sneeze
strawberrys
studants
necessary
snooze
sixtene
slushey
sientists

Name _____

Upside-Down View

The Opossum family spends all day upside down. Oftentimes, they are asleep.

When they wake up, they have a view of words that contain Os.

They like words with O, since they have some themselves!

Put the Os into all the words they see. This will help you spell those words right.

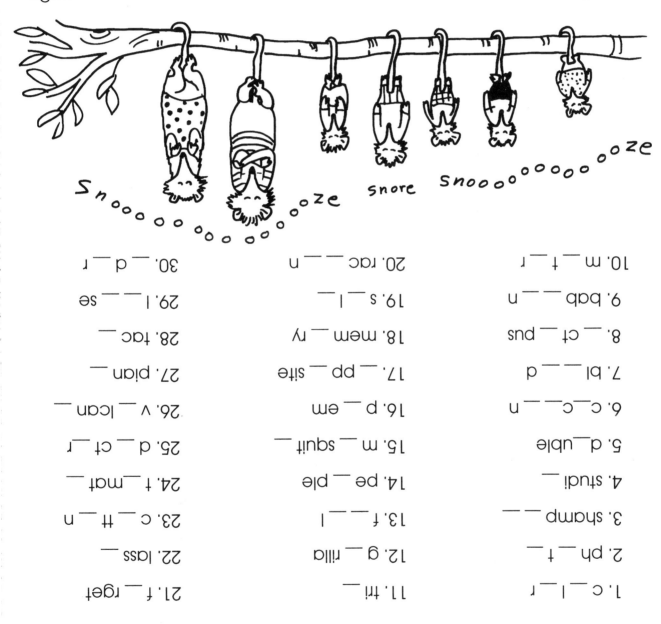

1. c__l__r
2. ph__t__
3. shamp__ __
4. studi__
5. d__uble
6. c__c__ n
7. bl__ __d
8. __ct__pus
9. bab__ __n
10. m__t__r

11. tr__ph__
12. grill__
13. f__l__
14. pe__ple
15. m__squit__
16. p__ em
17. __pp__site
18. mem__ry
19. __s__l
20. rac__ __ __n

21. f__rget
22. lass__
23. c__tt__n
24. t__mat__
25. d__ct__r
26. v__lcan__
27. pian__
28. tac__
29. l__ __se
30. d__ __r

Name _____

Quilting with Qs

Grandma Quail's quilt is full of words with the letter *q*. Can you spell them? Follow the clues to write a word that belongs in each square.

Then color the quilt.

If a square has a word that begins with *q*, color the square green. If *q* is not at the beginning of the word, color the square yellow.

qu__ __ **a short test**	qu __ __ __ **opposite of loud**	__qu__ __ __ **spray with water**	qu__ __ __ **partner to the king**
qu __ __ __ **sharp point on porcupine**	__qu__ __ __ **small forest animal with fluffy tail**	qu__ __ __ __ **an argument**	__qu __ __ __ **figure with 4 equal sides**
qu __ __ __ __ **shaking earth**	qu __ __ __ __ **four singers**	__qu __ __ __ **hold very tightly**	qu__ __ __ __ **25 cents**
qu __ __ __ __ **duck's sound**	__qu__ __ __ **wiggle**	qu __ __ **stop doing something**	__ qu __ __ __ **mouse's sound**
qu __ __ __ **fast**	qu __ __ __ __ __ **something you ask**	__qu__ __ __ __ **a yellow vegetable like pumpkin**	qu__ __ __ __ __ **answer in a division problem**

Name _____

Tracking Down W, X, Y, and Z

Sometimes words with *w, x, y,* or *z* can be tricky to spell.

Clever Detective Sherlock Foxy is tracking down some problem words with these letters. Every word has *w, x, y,* or *z.*

Fill in the missing letters in these words to spell them correctly.

1. We __ __ __ sday   2. wond __ rf __ l

3. waff __ __   4. __ __ isper

5. awf __ l   6. whol __

7. wick __ d

8. w __ __ stle

9. ex __ ept

10. ex __ ct   11. exp __ ct

12. mixt __ re   13. ex __ ra

14. ex __ iting   15. yo __ k

16. yaw___   17. yes __ __ __ day

18. r __ yme   19. s __ rup   20. cr __ zy

21. m __ stery   22. __ ize

23. __ ipper

24. doz __ n   25. fr __ __ __ ze

26. squ __ __ ze   27. fizz __   28. c __ zy

29. laz __   30. ye __ __ ow   31. j __ zz

32. __ ero   33. wea __ __ er   34. w __ w!

Name _____

Words with W, X, Y, or Z

Getting to Know BIG Words

Tiny Tina loves big words.
She has all of these huge words spelled right on her spelling test.
Answer the questions about Tina's favorite big words.

explosion

extraterrestrial

Mississippi

superhuman   ridiculous   kindergarten

EXCEPTIONAL   dictionary   multiplication

hippopotamus   earthworm   outrageous

somersault

tremendous   emergency   restaurant
underground

1. Which words have an ous ending?

_____

2. Which words have ion in them?

_____

3. Which words have the vowel combination au in them?

_____

4. Which words are compound words?

_____

5. Which word has 3 sets of double letters?

_____

Name _____

Basic Skills/Spelling 2-3

Getting to Know SMALL Words

Big Bruce Bear loves tiny words.
Unfortunately, his spelling is not as sharp as his claws!
Every word on Bruce's list is spelled wrong. Write each word correctly.

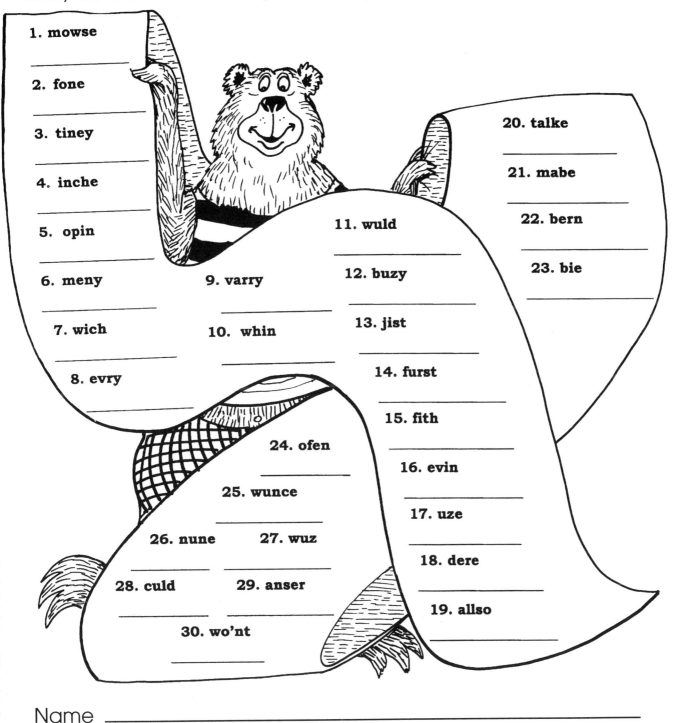

1. mowse

2. fone

3. tiney

4. inche

5. opin

6. meny

7. wich

8. evry

9. varry

10. whin

11. wuld

12. buzy

13. jist

14. furst

15. fith

16. evin

17. uze

18. dere

19. allso

20. talke

21. mabe

22. bern

23. bie

24. ofen

25. wunce

26. nune

27. wuz

28. culd

29. anser

30. wo'nt

Name _____

Names to Know

For her new computer game, Ella needs to know how to spell some important names of days, months, and holidays.

She has a start on these names. Help her finish them.

Write the missing word or word part to spell each word correctly.

NAME GAME

A. Days of the Week

S _____

M_____

T _____

W _____

T _____

F _____

S _____

B. Months

Jan_____

Feb_____

Au_____

Sep_____

Nov _____

C. Holidays

1) December day for presents

   _____

2) day for hearts and chocolates

   _____

3) a day to be thankful

   _____

4) U.S. Independence Day

   F_____ of J_____

5) day to celebrate mom

   M_____'s D_____

6) celebration of birthdays of George Washington and Abraham Lincoln

   Pr_____'s Day

Name _____

Places to Know

Look at all the places Wilbur wants to visit. Where will he go first?
He's checking the board to see what flights are leaving today.
OOPS! Some of the letters are missing from the place names.
Finish the names to spell them right.

DESTINATIONS

1. Dis_____land

2. Cal_____nia

3. N___ Y___k City

4. Golden Gate B_____

5. Mex_____

6. At_____ Ocean

7. P_____ Ocean

8. Fl_____da

9. Austr_____

10. C___ada

11. Wa_____ D.C.

12. M_____ W__ Galaxy

13. Grand C_____n

14. South _____ica

15. R_____y Mount___s

16. Ch_____ago

17. _____aska

18. Mount E_____st

19. S_____ Pole

20. Eur_____ (continent)

21. Af_____(continent)

22. Ant_____(continent)

Name _____

Basic Skills/Spelling 2-3

Proper Nouns

Cracking Some Tough Words

Chester has strong claws, but even he is having a hard time cracking these tough words today.

Help him decide which spelling is correct for each word.

Circle the correct spelling with a red marker or crayon.

Crustacean

1. a. choclate
   b. chocolate
   c. chocalate

2. a. vegtable
   b. vegetable
   c. vegatable

3. a. pepel
   b. peple
   c. people

4. a. suprize
   b. surprize
   c. surprise

5. a. scissors
   b. sissors
   c. scisors

6. a. tongue
   b. tonge
   c. tounge

7. a. memarize
   b. memorise
   c. memorize

8. a. bananna
   b. bannana
   c. banana

9. a. busness
   b. business
   c. buisness

10. a. twelfth
    b. twelth
    c. twelveth

11. a. friendly
    b. freindly
    c. friendley

12. a. lafter
    b. laufter
    c. laughter

13. a. adress
    b. address
    c. addres

14. a. puzzle
    b. puzzel
    c. puzel

15. a. calender
    b. callender
    c. calendar

16. a. suppoze
    b. suppose
    c. supose

17. a. kichen
    b. kitchin
    c. kitchen

18. a. regaler
    b. regular
    c. reguler

19. a. exercise
    b. exersise
    c. exercize

Name _____

Basic Skills/Spelling 2-3

Mouth-Watering Words

Chef Pierre is making a new menu for his sidewalk café.
Look at all the tasty foods he wants to serve to his guests!
Chef Pierre has some spelling problems in some of his
menu items. Find the items that have errors.
Write them CORRECTLY on the lines.

Chef Pierre's Café

MENU

cheeze sammiches
biscuits and jelly
pinapple drink
celary salid
cocanut pie
tomato sauce
spaghetti & meatballs
bannanna cream pie
fresh broccolli
ice cream
bacon & eggs
orange juice
milkshakes
burittos & taccos
hamburglers
maracaroni & cheese
pizza
suger cookies
chocalat cake
patatoe soop
sausage stew
lettuce and carrots
chicken and gravy

Name _____

Food Words

Words that Count

Mrs. Rabbit never loses count of her children.
How many children does she have?
Write the number (in words). _____
Write all of these numbers in words. Spell them carefully!

A. 1,000,000 _____

B. 1,000 _____

C. 500 _____

D. 101 _____

E. 13 _____

F. 40 _____

G. 55 _____

H. 77 _____

I. 38 _____

J. 19 _____

K. 14 _____

L. 80 _____

M. 16 _____

N. 67 _____

O. 2nd _____

P. 5th _____

Q. 3rd _____

R. 9th _____

Name _____

Number Words

Basic Skills/Spelling 2-3

Animal Spelling

Reba's telephone book has the names and numbers of all her animal friends.

Since she is a good speller, all the names are spelled right.

Angela Ant	445-2020	Lannie Lizard	622-0864
Cassie Cougar	662-1010	Moe Monkey	622-8653
Egbert Eagle	554-8763	Maurice Mule	445-1357
Ellie Elephant	622-9999	Ronald Rabbit	445-1065
Gonzo Giraffe	455-9753	Rebecca Raccoon	552-1753
Gus Grasshopper	662-9999	Reba Rattlesnake	552-8765
George Gorilla	455-9081	Ralph Rooster	999-9876
Gustus Goose	622-1111	Peter Parrot	224-0001
Gail Gopher	445-0897	Polly Porcupine	544-8675
Kit Kangaroo	455-5678	Todd Turtle	622-1975
Lonnie Lion	455-8888	Zoie Zebra	455-2468

Find the names that match these numbers.

Write the last name of the animal friend. Spell it right.

Usually an animal name does not need a capital letter, but these are the proper names of Reba's friends. So, begin each one with a capital letter.

A. 622-0864 _____

B. 662-9999 _____

C. 544-8675 _____

D. 455-5678 _____

E. 622-8653 _____

F. 622-9999 _____

G. 455-9753 _____

H. 552-1753 _____

I. 622-1975 _____

J. 554-8763 _____

K. 445-1065 _____

L. 224-0001 _____

M. 552-8765 _____

N. 445-0897 _____

O. 445-1357 _____

P. 455-2468 _____

Name _____

Animal Words

How's the Fishing?

How many fish has the Rabbit family hooked today?

Find out by looking for words that are spelled right.

Draw a line with a hook to "catch" each word that is spelled RIGHT.

How many did you catch? _____

- careful   • befour   • drawer   • trubble

- opin   accident   • bacon   • famus   • empty

- visiter   • evry   • voice   • uncle   • memary   • music

- somebody   • recess   • wiggel   • next   • arownd   • quiet

- length   • queston   • fourty   • just   • wether   • kitchen

- speshal   • cought   • heart   • nise   • wrong   • gladly

- ocean   • littel   • visiter   • does'nt   • odor   • natur

- puzzel   • taught   • pleaze   • wiegh

- musterd   • jelley   • hundred   • fever

Name _____

Identify Correctly-Spelled Words

Basic Skills/Spelling 2-3

Checking for Errors

Some of the words on Franky's checkerboard are spelled right.
Some of the words are spelled wrong.
In each square, circle the words spelled WRONG.
Use a red crayon or marker.
If a square has ONE wrong, color it BLUE.
If a square has TWO wrong, color it YELLOW.
If a square has THREE or more wrong, color it RED.

a. anamals addition alley arownd		**b.** basball batheing becuz beautiful	**c.** every always importent exactly
	d. diferent against figure possible	**e.** mountins usally measure mustard	
f. finaly sudenly building musik		**g.** circle bought clotheing puzzle	**h.** yellow general probaly dollar
	i. exercise million sombody regalar	**j.** eigher wether laddar famus	
k. laughed jealous quiet pleeze		**l.** togethar trubble choose vacation	**m.** captain election docter people
	n. expect sience freind resess	**o.** afraid suger cotten children	

Name _____

Identify Misspelled Words

Signs of Trouble

There's some trouble with the signs in the forest.
Bucky is having a hard time reading them because of the spelling errors.
Write the message from each sign for Bucky.
Use the lines below to write the messages. This time, spell all the words right.

1. _____
2. _____
3. _____
4. _____
5. _____
6. _____
7. _____
8. _____

Name _____

Conversations After Dark

These raccoon conversations have many words spelled wrong.
Listen in on their "talk" and find the errors.
Write each sentence over. Correct the spelling as you work!

_____   _____   _____
_____   _____   _____
_____   _____   _____
_____   _____   _____

_____   _____   _____
_____   _____   _____
_____   _____   _____
_____   _____   _____

Name _____

Identify Spelling Errors in Writing

Mistakes In the News

The news headlines are a bit confusing to Bruno this week.
Maybe it's because of all the spelling errors.
Fix the mistakes in the headlines.
Write each one over in the space below the headline.
Spell the words right!

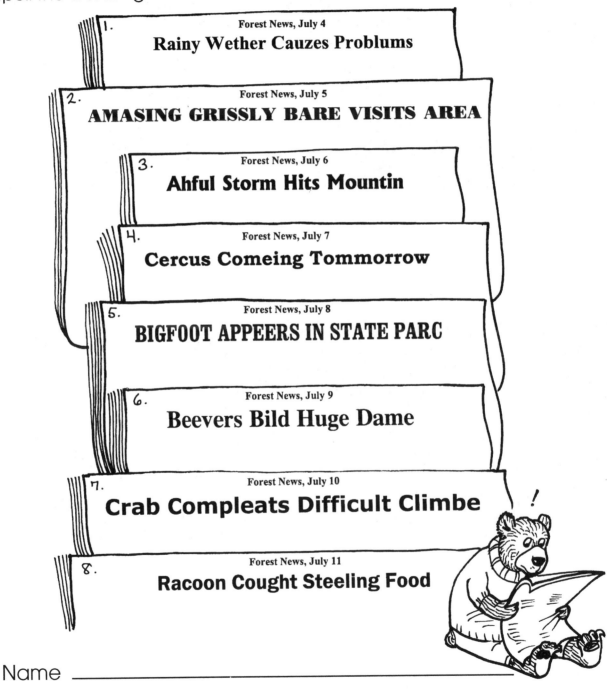

1. Forest News, July 4
   Rainy Wether Cauzes Problums

2. Forest News, July 5
   AMASING GRISSLY BARE VISITS AREA

3. Forest News, July 6
   Ahful Storm Hits Mountin

4. Forest News, July 7
   Cercus Comeing Tommorrow

5. Forest News, July 8
   BIGFOOT APPEERS IN STATE PARC

6. Forest News, July 9
   Beevers Bild Huge Dame

7. Forest News, July 10
   Crab Compleats Difficult Climbe

8. Forest News, July 11
   Racoon Cought Steeling Food

Name _____

Some Words That Give Spellers Trouble

about	chief	height	mystery	scissors	unusual
accident	chocolate	here	necessary	shoes	used
address	choose	honest	neighbor	since	usually
again	circle	hour	neither	some	vegetable
almost	climb	hundred	ninety	somebody	very
already	collar	hurried	none	stopped	voice
always	color	immediately	notice	straight	wear
among	coming	important	obey	sugar	weather
angel	could	island	often	sure	Wednesday
animal	country	instead	once	taught	weigh
appear	desert	juice	opposite	tear	where
answer	different	just	ought	their	whether
any	doctor	kitchen	pajamas	they	which
August	does	knew	paid	though	whistle
baking	done	knives	people	through	whole
balloon	don't	knock	picnic	tired	won't
banana	early	know	piece	tomorrow	would
beautiful	easy	language	please	tonight	write
because	empty	laugh	police	toward	writing
been	enough	lemon	practice	triangle	wrote
beginning	every	length	prize	trouble	yellow
believe	exercise	library	quarter	truly	your
bicycle	explain	Lincoln	question	Tuesday	you're
blue	February	listen	quiet	twelfth	
break	forget	loose	quite	two	
breakfast	forty	lose	rabbit		
breathe	fourth	lovely	raise		
built	friend	making	ready		
business	frighten	many	really		
busy	ghost	marshmallow	restaurant		
buy	guess	meant	rhyme		
cannot	hamburger	medal	said		
can't	having	minute	safety		
carrot	hear	mosquito	sandwich		
caught	heard	much	says		

Spelling Skills Test

Find the correct words in each row. Circle them.

1. dolar   zipper   hugging   gost
2. puddle   garadge   million   laugh
3. afraid   lemmon   appear   sumer
4. graph   quizes   cotton   friend

Circle the correct spelling.

5. absent   abcent
6. krayon   crayon
7. sise   size
8. jiraffe   giraffe

Write the correct contraction for each pair of words.

9. did not _____
10. she will _____
11. they are _____
12. I have _____

13. **Circle the words that have one or more silent letters.**

bottle   **rhyme**   dough
lumpy   **lamb**   ghost
bridge   halo   liver
wrap   **lonesome**
know   sword

shhhhh

Write ie or ei in each blank to spell the word correctly.

14. fr ____ nd   16. bel ____ ve
15. w ____ gh   17. p ____ ce

Choose a pair of vowels from the hat to spell each word correctly.

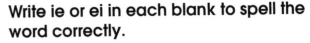

ai   ou   ee   ia   oo   oi   oa   ea   ui

18. m ____ ntain
19. r ____ ster
20. r ____ son
21. g ____ nt
22. sp ____ ch
23. motorb ____ t
24. r ____ se
25. b ____ ldings
26. n ____ se

Write the correct ending on each word: er, ar, or or

27. col _____   30. flav _____
28. doll _____   31. coll _____
29. nev _____   32. ladd _____

Write the correct ending on each word: y or ey

33. penn _____   36. monk _____
34. reall _____   37. hon _____
35. vall _____   38. cit _____

Write the plural form of each of these words. Write the whole word.

39. watch _____
40. quart _____

Name _____

Basic Skills/Spelling 2-3

41. candy _____

42. box _____

43. donkey _____

44. mouse _____

45. tooth _____

46. family _____

47. goose _____

48. **Circle the words on the trash can that are spelled correctly.**

garbige   judge

brige   cabbege

fudge   hedge

ridge   garadge

ledge

49. **Circle the words on the rock that are spelled correctly.**

tryed   wishd

caught   rubed

worryed   slipped

grabbed   getted

keeped   enjoyed

Write the past tense of each of these words. Write the whole word.

50. eat _____

51. hop _____

52. find _____

53. hurry _____

Add *ing* to each word. Write the whole word.

54. leap _____

55. hide _____

56. fly _____

57. swat _____

Add the suffix or ending. Write the whole word. Spell it right!

58. hot + er = _____

59. scare + y = _____

60. tiny + est = _____

61. care + less = _____

Choose a prefix from the poster to add to each word. Write the whole word.

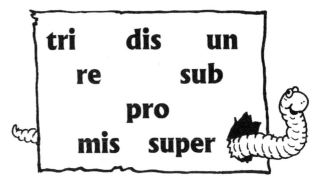

tri   dis   un

re   sub

pro

mis   super

62. angle _____

63. write _____

Name _____

Spelling Skills Test

64. tie   _____

65. marine   _____

66. take   _____

67. Mimi chose some wrong words when she wrote her story. **Circle the wrong words.**

Polly road along on an old hoarse threw the woulds. The hoarse tripped and lost a shoo in the creak. Polly fell off. Did she brake her tow?

68. Which of the bee's words are correct? **Circle them.**

none   once   choclat

people   forty   ocean

wheather   opin   voice

trubble

69. Which words are compound words? **Circle them.**

bedspread   homeless

disturb   campfire

nightgown   argument

reward   fingernail

Name _____

Circle the word in each group that is spelled wrong.

| 70. | syrup | success | fussy |
| | Friday | stranger | sience |

| 71. | surprise | sixtey | possible |
| | friend | messy | sentence |

| 72. | moter | doctor | cotton |
| | mystery | double | tomato |

| 73. | chocolate | around | vegetable |
| | different | Lincoln | memary |

| 74. | squirrel | squeak | quake |
| | questun | Africa | quietly |

• **tomatoe sause**

• **suger cookies**

• **cheese pissa**

• **lettice salid**

• **bannanna pie**

• **hamburglers**

The menu has some wrong spellings.

Write each food again. This time, spell it right.

75. _____

76. _____

77. _____

78. _____

79. _____

80. _____

Find the word that is spelled wrong. Write it correctly.

81. Cassie's friends were quiet mad at her.

_____

82. Felix can't remember witch path to take.

_____

83. Bruno already tired to open that door.

_____

84. **Circle the animal names that are spelled correctly.**

giraffe   ant   eagel

turtel   goose   monky

rooster   parrot   raccoon

Write these numbers in words.

85. 500 _____

86. 55 _____

87. 38 _____

88. 3rd _____

89. 19 _____

I ca'nt rember if I put jelley on my sammich.

90. **Write this quote again. Spell all the words correctly.**

_____

_____

_____

_____

Write each word correctly.

91. shood _____

92. Wensday _____

93. evry _____

94. brocken _____

95. littel _____

96. befour _____

97. pepel _____

98. Febuary _____

Write each headline again below it. Spell all the words right.

99.
Forest News, July 5
Fourty Millon Dollers Found in Garbidge

100.
Forest News, July 6
Ladder Falls on Anamal Docter

_____

_____

_____

_____

Name _____

Spelling Skills Test

Answer Key

Skills Test

1. zipper, hugging
2. puddle, million, laugh
3. afraid, appear
4. graph, cotton, friend
5. absent
6. crayon
7. size
8. giraffe
9. didn't
10. she'll
11. they're
12. I've
13. bottle, rhyme, dough, lamb, ghost, bridge, wrap, lonesome, know, sword
14. friend
15. weigh
16. believe
17. piece
18. ou
19. oo
20. ea
21. ia
22. ee
23. oa
24. ai
25. ui
26. oi
27. or
28. ar
29. er
30. or
31. ar
32. er
33. y
34. y
35. ey
36. ey
37. ey
38. y
39. watches
40. quarts
41. candies
42. boxes
43. donkeys
44. mice
45. teeth
46. families
47. geese
48. judge, fudge, hedge, ridge, ledge
49. caught, slipped, grabbed, enjoyed
50. ate
51. hopped
52. found
53. hurried
54. leaping
55. hiding
56. flying
57. swatting
58. hotter
59. scary
60. tiniest
61. careless
62. triangle
63. rewrite
64. untie or retie
65. submarine
66. mistake or retake
67. road, hoarse, threw, woulds, hoarse shoo, creak, brake, tow
68. none, once, people, forty, ocean, voice
69. bedspread, campfire, nightgown, fingernail
70. sience
71. sixtey
72. moter
73. memary
74. questun
75. tomato sauce
76. sugar cookies
77. cheese pizza
78. lettuce salad
79. banana pie
80. hamburgers
81. quite
82. which
83. tried
84. giraffe, ant, goose, rooster, parrot, raccoon
85. five hundred
86. fifty-five
87. thirty-eight
88. third
89. nineteen
90. I can't remember if I put jelly on my sandwich.
91. should
92. Wednesday
93. every
94. broken
95. little
96. before
96. people
97. February
99. Forty Million Dollars Found in Garbage
100. Ladder Falls on Animal Doctor

Skills Exercises

page 10

1 ll—dollar, swallow, million, follow, balloon, umbrella

2 nn—connect, tennis, penny, cannot, running, funny

3 ss—possible, scissors, guessing, messes, lesson

4 bb— dribble, rabbit, bubble, cabbage, ribbon

5 pp—happen, appear, clapped, hopping, zipper

6 ff— office, different, ruffle, fluffy, sniffle

7 gg—wiggle, soggy, hugging, goggles, muggy, giggle

8 mm— drummer, swimmer, humming, yummy, summer, trimmed

9 dd—fiddle, puddle, sudden, middle, muddy

10 rr—correct, parrot, carry, tomorrow, arrow

11 tt—cotton, button, matter, swatting, batted

12 zz—fuzzy, buzzing, fizzle, jazzy, quizzes

page 11

1. magic
2. surprise
3. circus
4. circle
5. crazy
6. size
7. absent
8. cloudy
9. giant
10. gym
11. jelly
12. giraffe
13. eyes
14. tease
15. catch
16. color
17. cool
18. city
19. crayon
20. gentle

page 12

Ralph's red rocks are:
phonics, geography, phrase, graph, photograph
Fulbright's blue rocks are:
daughter, though, laugh, tough, frighten, high, ghost

page 13

1. afternoon
2. breeze
3. doorknob
4. freezer
5. knee
6. oversleep
7. goose or geese
8. outdoors

9. choosy or cheesy
10. drool
11. rooster
12. squeeze
13. bloom
14. foolish
15. speech
16. cool
17. steep, or stoop
18. queen
19. raccoon
20. baboon
21. tooth or teeth
22. peek
23. loose
24. cartoon
25. school
26. balloon
27. cocoon

page 14

Sections containing these words should be colored:
lime, wife, tickle, lonely, halves, puzzle, froze, uncle, gone, scramble, cure, glue, cattle, ounce, maze, able, bottle, tone, argue, shine, ripe, lonesome, homework, beetle, shake

page 15

Words that should be circled in red:
lie, veil, vein, weight, their, piece, grieve, brief, eight, freight, believe, pie, reign, sleigh, die, neighborhood
1. height
2. weird
3. either
4. neither

Copyright ©2000 by Incentive Publications, Inc., Nashville, TN.
Basic Skills/Spelling 2-3

5. foreign
6. ceiling

page 16

Path should connect these words (not · necessarily in this order). The exact path a student chooses will vary.

about
fountain
cousin
ground
mouth
thought
sound
blouse
bought
shout
round
should
house
yours
scout

page 17

Words to be circled are:

1. coach
2. boast
3. coast
4. groaned
6. charcoal
10. load
12. oak
13. road
14. moaning
15. loan
16. toaster
19. throat
20. loaf
21. moat
23. motorboat
24. poach

page 18

The trail should connect these points (words) in this order:

Clue #1 - Check student maps to see that the trail begins at Cape Fear.

Clue #2 - early

Clue #3 - beard
Clue #4 - easy
Clue #5 - searching
Clue #6 - stealing
Clue #7 - bread
Clue #8 - seasons
Clue #9 - earthworm
Clue #10 - breathe
Clue #11 - weather
Clue # 12 - beach
    X should be on or near the word *beach*.

page 19

Down
1. raining
2. aunt
3. mail
4. glue
6. noise
8. frown
10. suit
11. soil
12. blue

Across
4. giant
5. buildings
7. point
9. raise
13. flows
14. tail

page 20

1. or
2. er
3. er
4. er
5. er
6. or
7. er
8. or
9. ar
10. or
11. er
12. ar
13. or
14. or
15. er
16. ar
17. or
18. er
19. er
20. or
21. er
22. er
23. er
24. or

page 21

1. age words:
    garbage
    garage
    courage
    manage
    cabbage
2. adge words:
    badge
3. edge words:
    ledge

hedge
pledge
4. idge words:
    bridge
    ridge
5. udge words:
    fudge
    judge
    budge

page 22

1. ey
2. y
3. y
4. y
5. y
6. ey
7. ey
8. y
9. y
10. y
11. y
12. ey
13. y
14. ey
15. y
16. ey
17. y
18. y

Color these starbursts yellow: 2, 3, 4, 5, 8, 9, 10, 11, 14,16, 17, 18
Color these purple: 1, 6, 7, 12, 13, 15

page 23

Cross out these words.
    never, liver, halo, wishes, cola, gasping, slippery, lumpy, whisper, whine
(Students may argue that whisper, whine, and slippery do have silent letters—these answers, therefore, may be counted either way.)

page 24

1. s
2. es
3. es
4. es
5. s
6. es
7. s
8. es
9. es
10. s
11. es
12. s
13. s
14. es
15. s
16. s
17. es
18. es

red, yellow, or blue: 1, 5, 7, 10, 12, 13, 15, 16
orange, purple, or

green: 2, 3, 4, 6, 8, 9, 11, 14, 17, 18

page 25

Kite # 1 should have these words written on the lines of its tail:
    teeth
    wolves
    knives
    women
    geese
    feet
    mice

Kite # 2 should have these words written on the lines of its tail:
    armies
    babies
    candies
    cities
    spies
    countries
    navies
    ladies
    families
    ponies
    bakeries
    parties

Kite # 3 should have these words written on the lines of its tail:
    keys
    valleys
    donkeys
    turkeys
    monkeys

page 26

1. grabbed
2. shouted
3. jumped
4. fished
5. hurried
6. climbed
7. smelled
8. chewed
9. cooked
10. stirred
11. rubbed
12. tried
13. followed
14. wished
15. denied
16. sniffed
17. worried
18. slipped
19. rested

20. trimmed
21. robbed
22. enjoyed
23. laughed

page 27

1. slid
2. left
3. kept
4. shook
5. bit
6. ate
7. chose
8. built
9. taught
10. caught
11. found
12. lost
13. saw
14. hid

page 28

1. leaping
2. waving
3. laughing
4. swatting
5. screaming
6. gripping
7. opening
8. hollering
9. running
10. squeezing
11. writing
12. stirring
13. hiding
14. climbing
15. worrying

page 29

1. sweeter, sweetest
2. tastier, tastiest
3. bigger, biggest
4. grumpier, grumpiest
5. fuller, fullest
6. greater, greatest
7. stickier, stickiest
8. hotter, hottest
9. fluffier, fluffiest
10. taller, tallest

page 30

A. submarine
B. describe
C. untie
D. mistake
E. bicycle

F. antigerm
G. explain
H. minivan
I. triangle
J. rewrite
K. internet
L. impolite
M. preview
N. disobey
O. nonfat
P. semicircle

page 31

1. scary
2. actor
3. different
4. tropical
5. lonely
6. careless
7. friendliness
8. troublesome
9. famous
10. shiniest
11. frighten
12. likable
13. fancier
14. selfish
15. forgetful
16. friendship

page 32

1. choose
2. pale
3. groan
4. so
5. fur
6. see
7. toe
8. paws
9. ants
10. sense
11. prints
12. road
13. shoe
14. berry

page 33

Words from story that should be circled and re-written (The words do not need to be in this order):
board—bored
wood—would
meat—meet
write—right

ate—eight
creak—creek
weight—wait
knot—not
threw—through
beet—beat
maid—made
tale—tail
eye—I
knight—night
pare—pair
buy—by
their—there

page 34

A. water
B. finger
C. rain
D. bed
E. sand
F. shoe
G. any
H. sea
I. home

page 35

1. night: nightmare, overnight, nightgown, nighttime, nightlight
2. out: campout, outside, outdoors, knockout, without
3. camp: campfire, campground, campsite
4. light: sunlight, lighthouse, flashlight, daylight, lightweight
5. under: underwater, underground, underline, underpants
6. down: sundown, downtown, downstairs, downpour
7. book: bookworm,

bookstore, bookcase, cookbook
8. snow: snowflake, snowman, snowball, showshoes
9. door: outdoor, doorstep, doorbell, doorway
10. sun: sunlight, sundown, sunburn, sunset, sunflower

page 36

1. you're
2. I've
3. won't
4. she'd
5. let's
6. weren't
7. who'll
8. wasn't
9. what's
10. we're
11. we'd
12. didn't
13. it'll
14. couldn't
15. that's
16. you'll
17. they're
18. can't
19. he'll
20. doesn't

page 37

1. Which
2. tired
3. quiet
4. dessert
5. weather
6. from
7. except
8. through
9. carton
10. recipe
11. colors
12. diary

page 38

The correctly spelled words are:

sassy, sneeze, hissing, sausage, disease, Mississippi, snooze, necessary, fussy, scissors, sword
These should be colored green. They form a snake.

page 39

1. color
2. photo
3. shampoo
4. studio
5. double
6. cocoon
7. blood
8. octopus
9. baboon
10. motor
11. trio
12. gorilla
13. fool
14. people
15. mosquito
16. poem
17. opposite
18. memory
19. solo
20. racoon
21. forget
22. lasso
23. cotton
24. tomato
25. doctor
26. volcano
27. piano
28. taco
29. loose
30. odor

page 40

Words in the quilt should be:
Row 1 quiz, quiet, squirt, queen
Row 2 quill, squirrel, quarrel, square
Row 3 quake, quartet, squeeze, quarter
Row 4 quack, squirm, quit, squeak
Row 5 quick, question, squash, quotient

page 41

1. Wednesday
2. wonderful
3. waffle
4. whisper
5. awful
6. whole
7. wicked
8. whistle
9. except
10. exact
11. expect
12. mixture
13. extra
14. exciting
15. yolk
16. yawn
17. yesterday
18. rhyme
19. syrup
20. crazy
21. mystery
22. prize or size
23. zipper
24. dozen
25. freeze
26. squeeze
27. fizzy
28. cozy
29. lazy
30. yellow
31. jazz
32. zero
33. weather
34 wow

page 42

1. tremendous, ridiculous, outrageous
2. explosion, dictionary, exceptional, multiplication
3. restaurant, somersault
4. earthworm, underground, superhuman, extraterrestrial
5. Mississippi

page 43

1. mouse
2. phone
3. tiny

Basic Skills/Spelling 2-3

4. inch
5. open
6. many
7. which or witch
8. every
9. very or vary
10. when or win
11. would or wood
12. busy
13. just
14. first
15. fifth
16. even
17. use
18. deer or dear
19. also
20. talk
21. maybe
22. burn or born or barn
23. buy or by or bye
24. often
25. ounce or once
26. none or nun or noon
27. was
28. could or cold
29. answer
30. won't

page 44

A. Sunday, Monday, Tuesday, Wednesday, Thursday, Friday, Saturday
B. January, February, August, September, November
C. 1. Christmas or Hanukkah
2. Valentine's Day
3. Thanksgiving
4. Fourth of July
5. Mother's Day
6. President's Day

page 45

1. Disneyland
2. California
3. New York City
4. Golden Gate Bridge
5. Mexico
6. Atlantic Ocean
7. Pacific Ocean
8. Florida
9. Australia
10. Canada
11. Washington D.C.
12. Milky Way Galaxy
13. Grand Canyon
14. South America or Africa
15. Rocky Mountains
16. Chicago
17. Alaska
18. Mount Everest
19. South Pole
20. Europe
21. Africa
22. Antarctica

page 46

1. b	8. c	15. c
2. b	9. b	16. b
3. c	10. a	17. c
4. c	11. a	18. b
5. a	12. c	19. a
6. a	13. b	
7. c	14. a	

page 47

Items that have errors, corrected:
cheese sandwiches
pineapple drink
celery salad
coconut pie
banana cream pie
fresh broccoli
burritos & tacos
hamburgers
macaroni & cheese
sugar cookies
chocolate cake
potato soup

page 48

There are twenty seven rabbit children.
A. one million
B. one thousand
C. five hundred
D. one hundred one
E. thirteen
F. forty
G. fifty-five
H. seventy-seven
I. thirty-eight
J. nineteen
K. fourteen
L. eighty
M. sixteen
N. sixty-seven
O. second
P. fifth
Q. third
R. ninth

page 49

A. Lizard
B. Grasshopper
C. Porcupine
D. Kangaroo
E. Monkey
F. Elephant
G. Giraffe
H. Raccoon
I. Turtle
J. Eagle
K. Rabbit
L. Parrot
M. Rattlesnake
N. Gopher
O. Mule
P. Zebra

page 50

There are 23 correct words including the example done for students. Correct words that should have a hook & line drawn to them:
accident
careful
drawer
bacon
empty
voice
uncle
music
somebody
recess
next
quiet
length
just
kitchen
heart
wrong
gladly
ocean
odor
taught
hundred
fever

page 51

Wrong words listed below, as well as color which student should use for square.
a. yellow: anamals, arownd
b. red: basball, batheing, becuz
c. blue: important
d. blue: diferent
e. yellow: mountins, usally
f. red: finaly, sudenly, musik
g. blue: clotheing
h. blue: probaly
i. yellow: sombody, regalar
j. red: eigher, wether, laddar, famus
k. blue: pleeze
l. yellow: togethar, trubble
m. blue: docter
n. red: sience, friend, resess
o. yellow: suger, cotton

page 52

1. Please put garbage in the barrel.
2. Be careful with matches.
3. Watch out for falling rocks.
4. No shouting allowed in forest!
5. Broken bridge may be dangerous!
6. Loud noises bother the animals.
7. Beware! The blueberries are poison.
8. Tonight's forest walk is canceled.

page 53

TOP, left to right:

Could you give me your exact address, please?

That's impossible! I don't live anywhere.

Oh, you just don't want anyone to bother you.

BOTTOM, left to right:

Go straight to bed without your supper.

Why? Did I do something wrong?

Yes, you ate my favorite pumpkin pie that I had been saving for weeks!

page 54

1. Rainy Weather Causes Problems
2. Amazing Grizzly Bear Visits Area
3. Awful Storm Hits Mountain
4. Circus Coming Tomorrow
5. Bigfoot Appears in State Park
6. Beavers Build Huge Dam
7. Crab Completes Difficult Climb
8. Raccoon Caught Stealing Food